AF222298

# Mini Maestro

## Volume 2 / Band 2

50 Little Piano Pieces from Baroque to Modern Music
for Concerts, Lessons and Exams
50 kleine Klavierstücke vom Barock bis zur Moderne
für Konzert, Unterricht und Prüfungen

easy / leicht

Edited by / Herausgegeben von
Hans-Günter Heumann

Cover Illustration: Selina Peterson

**ED 23199**
ISMN 979-0-001-20882-6
ISBN 978-3-7957-1907-4

Volume 1 / Band 1:
ED 23198

Volume 3 / Band 3:
ED 23200

# Preface

The three-volume collection *Mini Maestro* presents little piano pieces advancing progressively from very easy to intermediate level, presented in chronological order across five centuries from the Baroque, Classical, Romantic and Modern eras through to jazz, pop and minimal music. At the end of each volume – under the heading *More fun to play together* – there are three additional pieces for piano duet. All the pieces are easy to learn and offer varied repertoire as an ideal supplement to any piano tutorial method with music suitable for concert performance, tuition purposes, examinations and competitions.

Children, adolescents or adults: anyone can be a Mini Maestro!

Enjoy yourself on the concert stage!
Hans-Günter Heumann

**Book 1** contains pieces in the five-finger range at various pitches, followed by pieces spanning an octave range with simple rhythms and easy chord sequences. Also featured are differing styles of articulation, melody in the left hand, octave or *ottava* signs, pieces in major and minor keys with key signatures of up to one sharp or flat.

**Book 2** contains pieces with an extended range of two octaves and chord sequences with three or four parts, including inversions. Other features include using the pedal, simple ornaments, basic polyphony, differentiating melody and accompaniment, pieces in major and minor keys with key signatures of up to two sharps or flats.

**Book 3** contains pieces with a range of up to four octaves with more demanding rhythms and speeds. Also included are subtle contrasts in tone, playing with expression, playing more than one part with one hand and advanced polyphony in major and minor keys with key signatures of up to three sharps or flats.

# Vorwort

Die dreibändige Sammlung *Mini Maestro* präsentiert sehr leichte bis mittelschwere, progressiv ange-ordnete kleine Klavierstücke aus 5 Jahrhunderten in chronologischer Reihenfolge von Barock, Klassik, Romantik, Moderne bis hin zu Jazz, Pop und Minimal Music. Das Ende eines jeden Bandes bilden – unter dem Motto *Zu Zweit mehr Spaß* – jeweils drei vierhändige Bonusstücke. Alle Spielstücke sind leicht zu erlernen und bieten ein vielfältiges Repertoire als ideale Ergänzung zu jeder Klavierschule, geeignet für Konzert, Unterricht, Prüfungen sowie Wettbewerbe.

Ob Kind, Jugendlicher oder Erwachsener: Jeder kann ein *Mini Maestro* sein!

Viel Erfolg auf der Konzertbühne wünscht
Hans-Günter Heumann

**Band 1** enthält Stücke im Fünftonraum/in wechselnden Fünftonräumen, danach Stücke im Oktavraum mit einfacher Rhythmik und leichtem Akkordspiel. Weitere Kriterien sind die unterschiedliche Artikulation, Melodie in der linken Hand, Oktavierungszeichen und Dur-/Mollstücke bis zu einem Kreuz-/B-Vorzeichen.

**Band 2** enthält Stücke im erweiterten Tonumfang von zwei Oktaven und drei- bis vierstimmigem Akkord-spiel mit Umkehrungen. Weitere Kriterien sind das Pedalspiel, elementare Verzierungen, einfache Polypho-nie, Differenzierung von Melodie und Begleitung und Dur-/Mollstücke bis zu zwei Kreuz-/B-Vorzeichen.

**Band 3** enthält Stücke bis zu vier Oktaven Tonumfang, anspruchsvollere Rhythmik und Geläufigkeit. Weitere Kriterien sind subtile klangliche Differenzierungen, ausdrucksvolles Spiel, Mehrstimmigkeit in einer Hand, fortgeschrittene Polyphonie sowie Dur-/Mollstücke bis zu drei Kreuz-/B-Vorzeichen.

# Contents / Inhalt

# Air

John Blow
1649–1708

# Minuet A minor

## Menuett a-Moll

Johann Krieger
1651–1735

from / aus: J. Krieger, 6 Musical Partitas / 6 musikalische Partiten

8

# Minuet G major

## Menuett G-Dur

### BWV Anh. 114

Christian Petzold
1677–1733

**3**

In the past this Minuet was attributed to J. S. Bach, as it is part of the Notebook for Anna Magdalena Bach, Schott ED 2698
Dieses Menuett wurde früher J. S. Bach zugeschrieben. Es steht im Notenbüchlein für Anna Magdalena Bach, Schott ED 2698

# Minuet G minor

## Menuett g-Moll
### BWV Anh. 115

Christian Petzold

In the past this Minuet was attributed to J. S. Bach, as it is part of the Notebook for Anna Magdalena Bach, Schott ED 2698
Dieses Menuett wurde früher J. S. Bach zugeschrieben. Es steht im Notenbüchlein für Anna Magdalena Bach, Schott ED 2698

# Aria

## D minor / d-Moll

### BWV 515

Johann Sebastian Bach
1685–1750

from / aus: Notebook for Anna Magdalena Bach / Notenbüchlein für Anna Magdalena, Schott ED 2698

# Praeludium

## C major / C-Dur

### BWV 939

Johann Sebastian Bach

from / aus: J. S. Bach, 12 little Preludes / 12 kleine Präludien, Schott ED 0849

# Gavotte

## C major / C-Dur

Georg Friedrich Händel
1685–1759

**7**

# Passepied

## C major / C-Dur
### HWV 559

Georg Friedrich Händel

# German Dance D major

## Deutscher Tanz D-Dur

Hob. IX:22/2

Joseph Haydn
1732–1809

# Minuet F major

## Menuett F-Dur
### Hob. IX:8/12

Joseph Haydn

from / aus: J. Haydn, 12 Menuets pour le Clavecin ou Pianoforte, Hob. IX:8

# Minuet F major

## Menuett F-Dur
### KV 2

Wolfgang Amadeus Mozart
1756–1791

from / aus: The Young Mozart / Der junge Mozart, Schott ED 9008

# Allegro

## B♭major / B-dur
### KV 3

Wolfgang Amadeus Mozart

from / aus: The Young Mozart / Der junge Mozart, Schott ED 9008

# German Dance C major

## Deutscher Tanz C-Dur
### WoO 8/1

Ludwig van Beethoven
1770–1827

# Ecossaise

## G major / G-Dur
### WoO 23

Ludwig van Beethoven

# Tempo di Menuetto

## Op. 125/8

Anton Diabelli
1781–1858

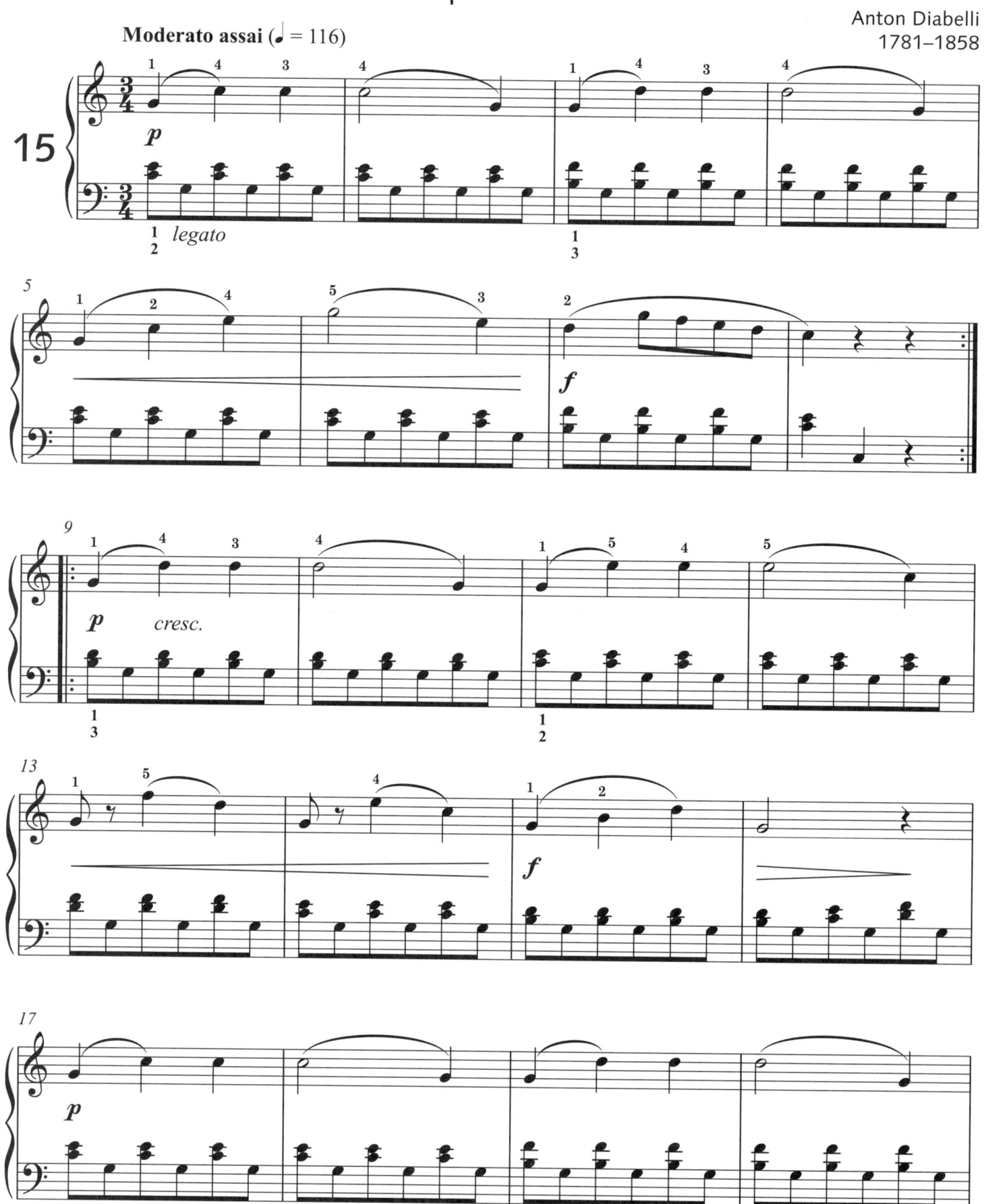

from / aus: A. Diabelli, The First Lessons at the Pianoforte / Die ersten Lektionen am Pianoforte, Op. 125

*Fine*

**Trio**

*Menuetto da capo*

# Vivace

## Op. 125/7

Anton Diabelli

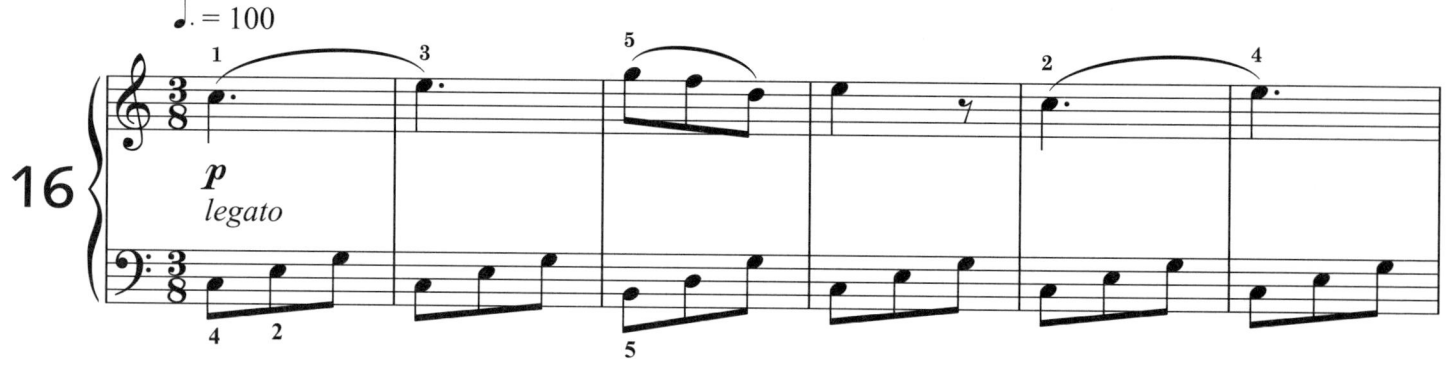

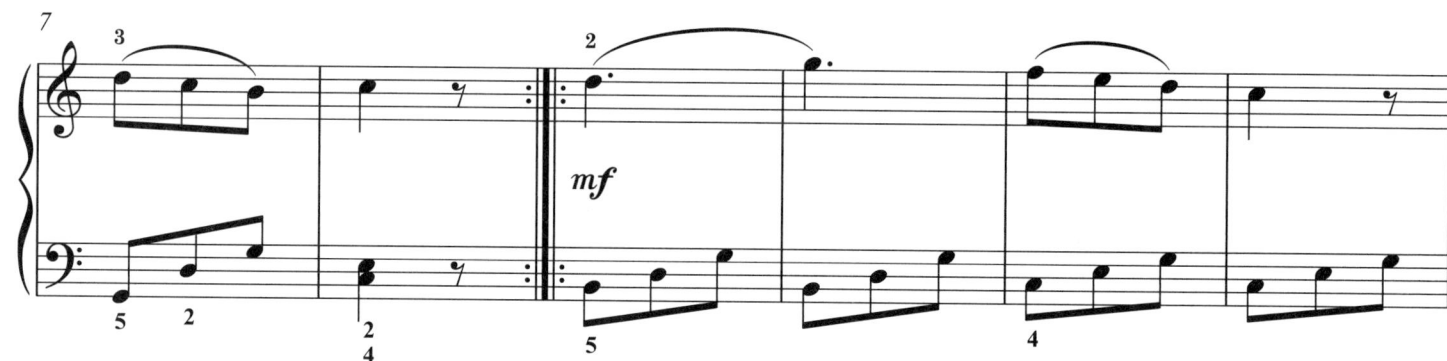

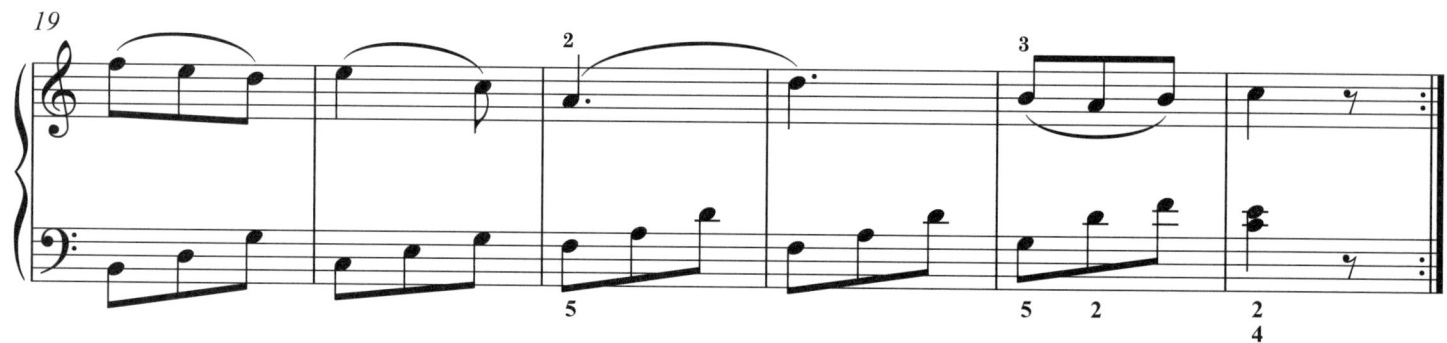

from / aus: A. Diabelli, The First Lessons at the Pianoforte / Die ersten Lektionen am Pianoforte, Op. 125

# Two Scottish Dances

## Zwei schottische Tänze

### No. 2 / Nr. 2

Friedrich Kuhlau
1786–1832

from / aus: F. Kuhlau, 6 Scottish Dances for Piano / 6 schottische Tänze für Klavier

### No. 5 / Nr. 5

Friedrich Kuhlau

from / aus: F. Kuhlau, 6 Scottish Dances for Piano / 6 schottische Tänze für Klavier

# Allemande

## Op. 4/2

Carl Maria von Weber
1786–1826

*D.C. al Fine*

# Mazurka

Maria Szymanowska
1789–1831

Fine

D.C. al Fine

# Scherzo
## Op. 55/3

Ignaz Moscheles
1794–1870

from / aus: I. Moscheles, Bonbonnière musicale, Op. 55

# Little Piece

## Stückchen
### Op. 68/5

Robert Schumann
1810–1856

from / aus: R. Schumann, Album for the Young / Album für die Jugend, Op. 68

# Air arabe

## Arabian Air / Arabische Melodie

Félix Le Couppey
1811–1887

from / aus: F. Le Couppey, L'ABC du Piano

# Piano Piece

## Klavierstück
### Op. 179/22

Cornelius Gurlitt
1820–1901

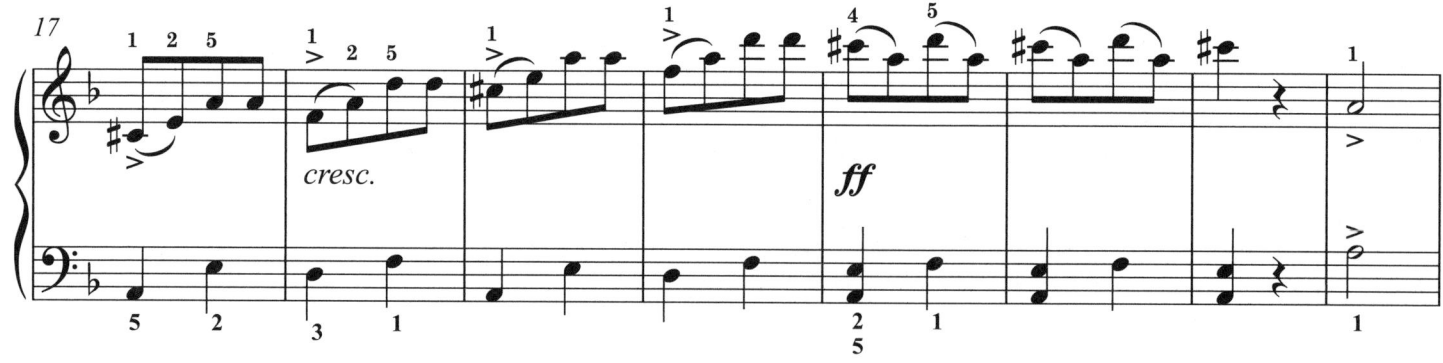

from / aus: C. Gurlitt, The Kindergarten / Der Kindergarten, Op. 179

# Gavotte

## Op. 210/9

Cornelius Gurlitt

D.C. al Fine

from / aus: C. Gurlitt, The First Performance / Der erste Vortrag, Op. 210

# Song

## Lied

### Serenade 1, Op. 183

Carl Reinecke
1824–1910

**Andante con moto** (♩ = 108)

from / aus: C. Reinecke, 5 Serenades for the Young / 5 Serenaden für die Jugend, Op. 183

# Scherzino

Eduard Horák
1839–1892

from / aus: E. Horák, Children's Piano School / Kinder-Klavierschule, Op. 112

# Sonatina C major

## Sonatine C-Dur
### Op. 30/4

Oskar Bolck
1839–1888

from / aus: O. Bolck, 6 Instructive Sonatinas / 6 instruktive Sonatinen, Op. 30

# Tarantella

Frederick Scotson Clark
1840–1883

# The Sick Doll

## Die kranke Puppe
### Op. 39/6

Peter Iljitsch Tschaikowsky
1840–1893

from / aus: P. I. Tschaikowsky, Children's Album / Kinderalbum, Op. 39, Schott UT 50134

# A Little Dance

## Ein kleines Tänzchen
### Op. 98/10

Alexander Gretchaninoff
1864–1956

from / aus: A. Gretchaninoff, Children's Book / Das Kinderbuch, Op. 98, Schott ED 1100

# After the Ball

## Nach dem Balle
### Op. 98/13

**Tempo di Mazurka** (♩ = 132)
*Dreamingly/ träumerisch*

Alexander Gretchaninoff

from / aus: A. Gretchaninoff, Children's Book / Das Kinderbuch, Op. 98, Schott ED 1100

# Waltz

## Walzer
### Op. 28/5

Samuil Maikapar
1867–1938

from / aus: S. Maikapar, Biriulki, Op. 28

# Play
## Spiel

Béla Bartók
1881–1945

from / aus: B. Bartók, For Children I, No. 5 / Für Kinder I, Nr. 5

# Melancholy
## Wehmut

Béla Bartók

from / aus: B. Bartók, For Children III, No. 7 / Für Kinder III, Nr. 7

# Waltz

## Walzer

Béla Bartók

from / aus: B. Bartók, Piano Tutor / Klavierschule

# Piano Study

## Klavier-Übung
### No. 20

Carl Orff
1895–1982

from / aus: C. Orff, Piano Study / Klavier-Übung, Schott ED 3561

# Simply Blue

John Kember
*1935

**40**

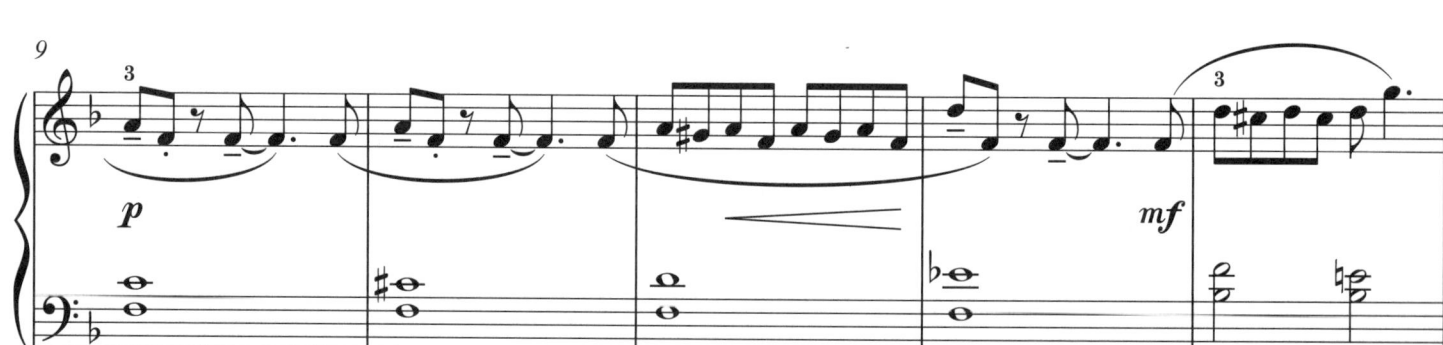

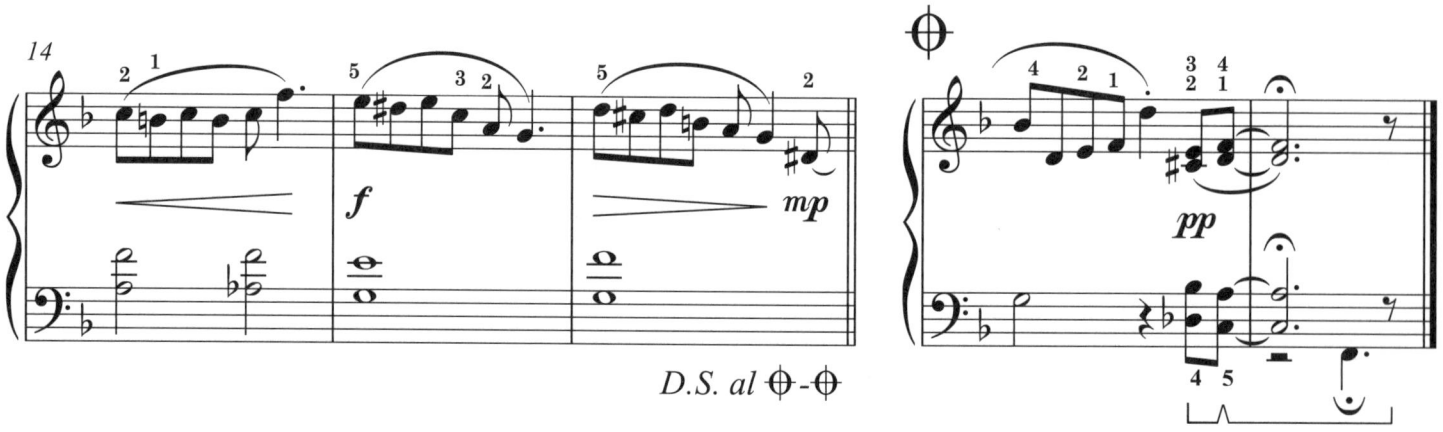

*D.S. al ⊕-⊕*

from / aus: J. Kember, On the Lighter Side, Blues Pieces for Piano solo, Schott ED 12726

# Lively Conversation

## Lustige Unterhaltung

Loris Tjeknavorian
*1937

**41**

from / aus: L. Tjeknavorian, Piano Workshop Vol. 1, Schott ED 8091

# When Paris Dreams

## Wenn Paris träumt

George Nevada
1939–2014

from / aus: G. Nevada, Romantic Miniatures / Romantische Miniaturen, Schott ED 7696

# Feelin' Groovy

Jürgen Moser
*1949

from / aus: J. Moser, Beginning Rock Piano, Schott ED 9503

# A Song of Hope

Rainer Mohrs
*1953

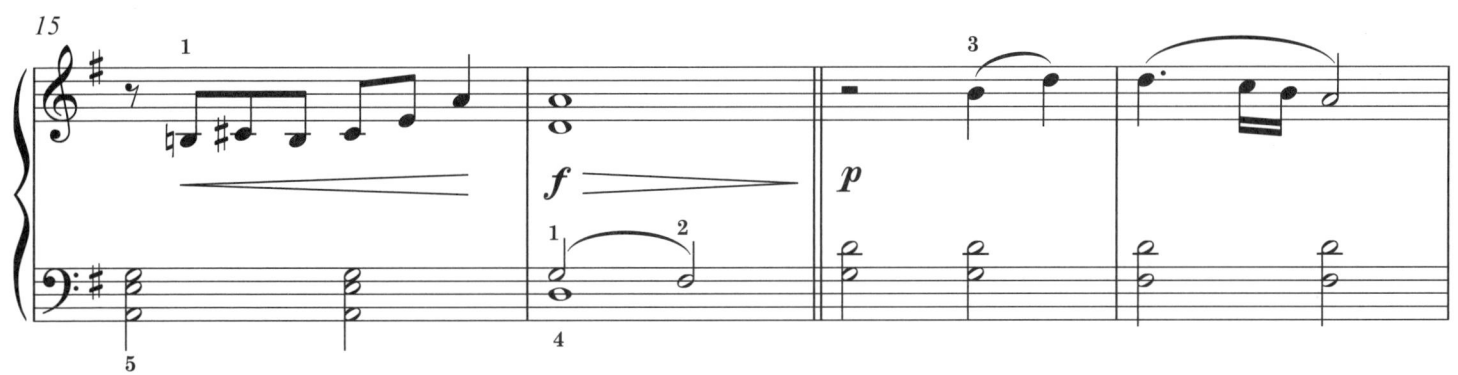

# Cool Jazz Cats

Hans-Günter Heumann
*1955

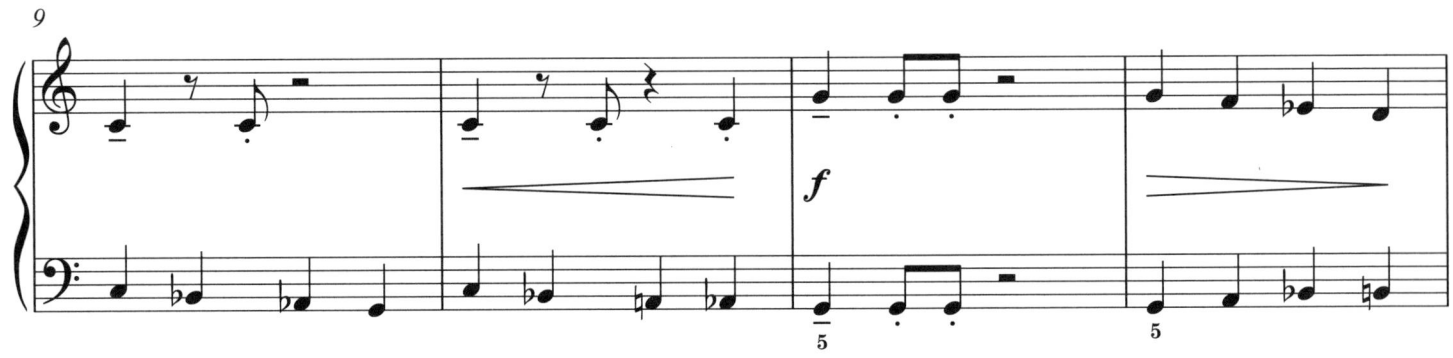

from / aus: H.-G. Heumann, Piano Playground 2 / Spielplatz Klavier 2, Schott ED 23048

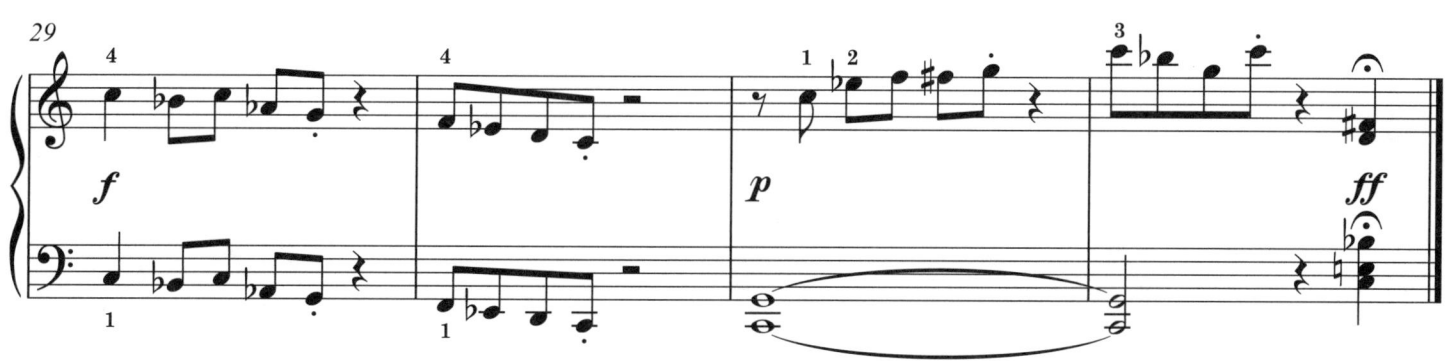

# Magic Piano

Hans-Günter Heumann

# Rainbow Fairy

## Regenbogen-Fee

Hans-Günter Heumann

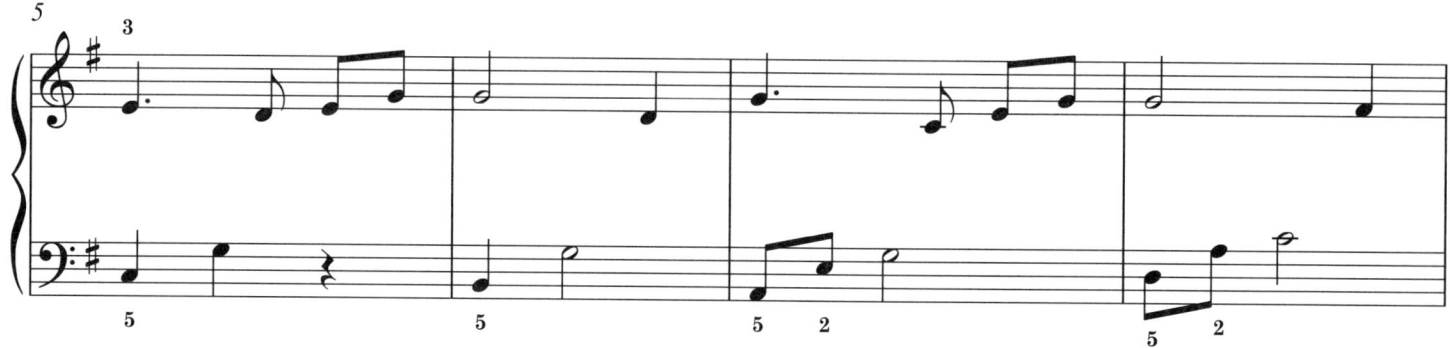

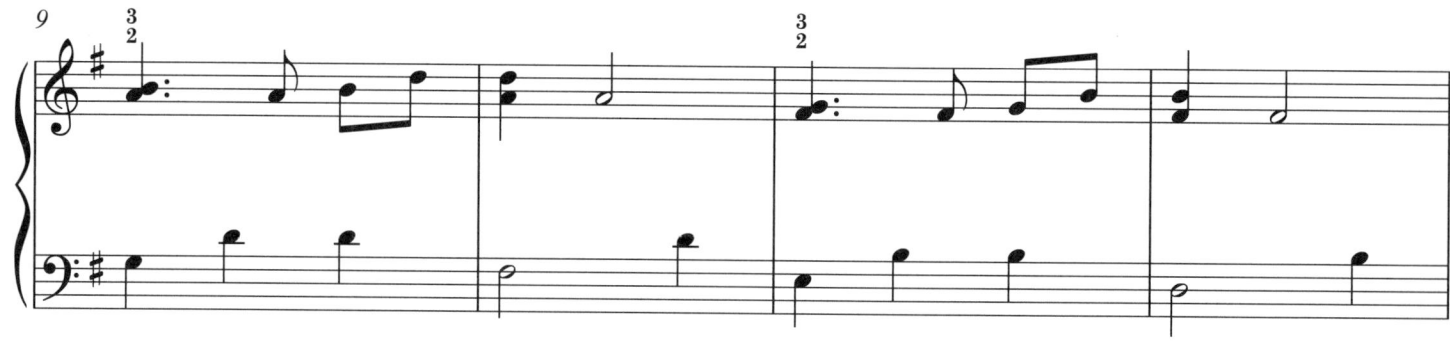

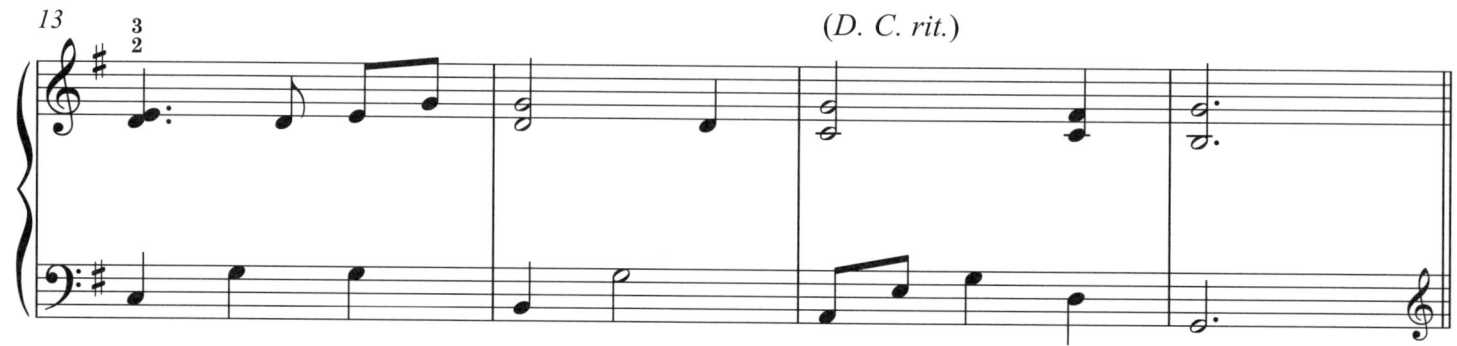

from / aus: H.-G. Heumann, Fantasy Piano, Schott ED 22111

*Fine*

*D.C al Fine*

# Modern Sonatina

## 1 À la Clementi

Hans-Günter Heumann

from / aus: H.-G. Heumann, R. Mohrs, Modern Piano, Schott ED 21128

## 2 Pop Ballad

# 3 Boogie-Woogie

# Scherzo
## Op. 149/6

Anton Diabelli
1781–1858

Trio
C minor / c-Moll

*Scherzo da capo al Fine*

from / aus: A. Diabelli, Melodious Exercises / Melodische Übungsstücke, Op. 149, Schott ED 9009

# Scherzo
## Op. 149/6

Anton Diabelli
1781–1858

**Trio**
C minor / c-Moll

*Scherzo da capo al Fine*

© 2019 Schott Music GmbH & Co. KG, Mainz

from / aus: A. Diabelli, Melodious Exercises / Melodische Übungsstücke, Op. 149, Schott ED 9009

# Ländler
## D 366/5

Franz Schubert
1797–1828
Arr.: Johannes Brahms (1833–1897)

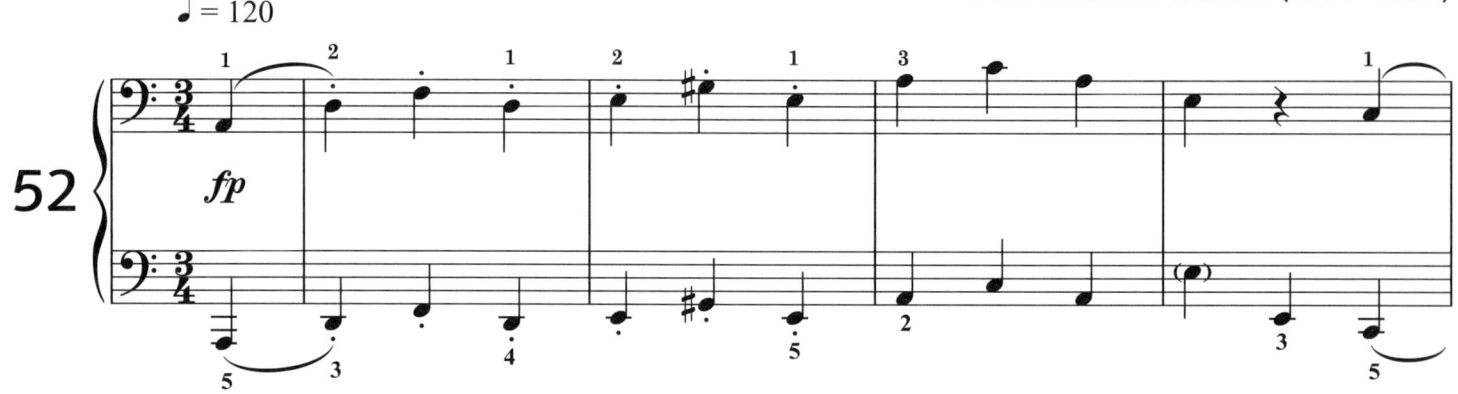

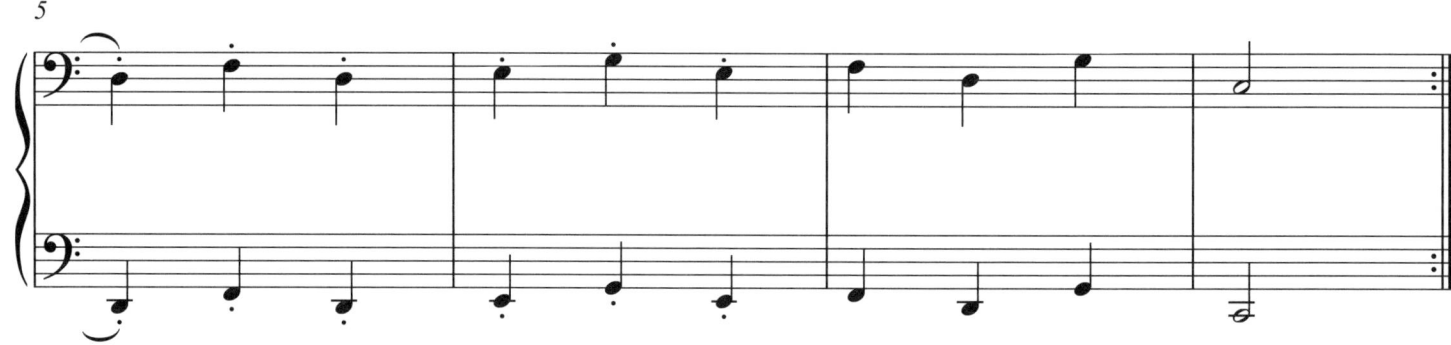

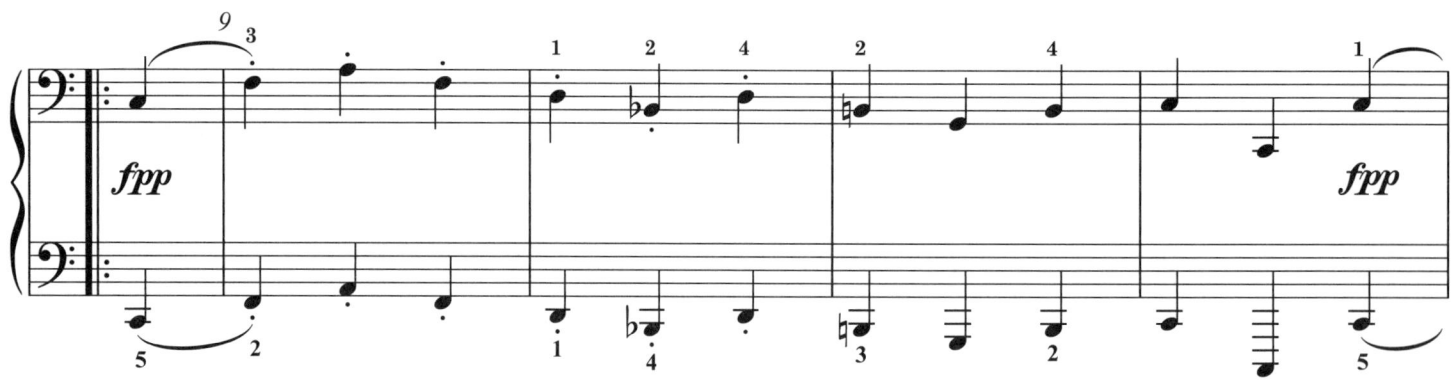

from / aus: F. Schubert, 11 Ländler, Schott ED 2338

# Ländler

## D 366/5

Franz Schubert
1797–1828
Arr.: Johannes Brahms (1833–1897)

from / aus: F. Schubert, 11 Ländler, Schott ED 2338

Secondo

# Fips in the Park *)

Mike Schoenmehl
*1957

from / aus: M. Schoenmehl, Jazz for Two, Schott ED 7990

*) Fips = Name of a monkey / Name eines Affen

# Fips in the Park*⁾

Mike Schoenmehl
*1957

from / aus: M. Schoenmehl, Jazz for Two, Schott ED 7990

*⁾ Fips = Name of a monkey / Name eines Affen

*) to be played less, e.g: meno forte = less loud / weniger laut

Schott Music, Mainz 59 639